Caterpillar

by Jo Sumara
illustrated by Bob Holt

Orlando   Boston   Dallas   Chicago   San Diego

A caterpillar crawled
on a leaf to eat.
He wore 60 shoes
on his 60 feet.

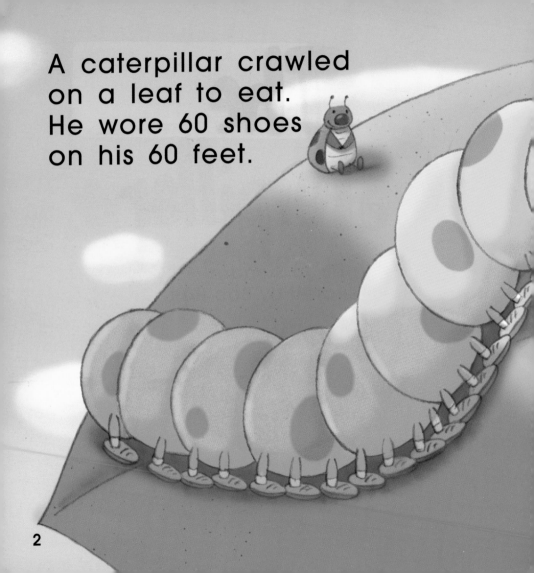

How long will it take me to
tie all my shoes?
A minute? An hour?
Oh, this is bad news!

The caterpillar sat down
and started his chore.
Soon his fingers
began to get sore.

This is going to take more
than a minute or two.
It may be an hour
before I get through!

The caterpillar's barber
went click, clack, click, clack!
How long would that short hair
take to grow back?

Would it take all week
or only a day,
or more like a month
to look his old way?

The caterpillar looked
each day to see
if his hair was as long
as it used to be.

8

It did take more
than a week or two.
It was more like a month
before his hair grew.

The caterpillar's mom
had something to say.
She told him tomorrow
would be his birthday.

How long had it been
since his last birthday cake?
From birthday to birthday
how long does it take?

He looked at the calendar.
The answer was clear.
From birthday to birthday
takes one full year.